OPENCAST COAL

COAL
Plant & Equipment

Bill Huxley

First published in 1993 by **Roundoak Publishing,
Nynehead, Wellington, Somerset, England, TA21 0BX**

© **Copyright 1993** Bill Huxley & Roundoak Publishing

ISBN 1 871565 12 X

Design & typesetting by **Haight Ashbury Design,
Stoke sub Hamdon, Somerset**

Printed in Great Britain by **Ian Allan Printing Limited,
Addlestone, Surrey**

Front cover: *'Big John' one of the two 1260W machines operated at Coalfield North by the C.P. Holdings Group which encompasses Shand Mining, Currall Lewis & Martin Ltd., Dygor-Gaylord, W.J. Simms, Sons & Cooke Ltd. and Murphy Bros. Ltd. The truck to the left of the bucket is one of the fleet of 8x8 Terberg coal trucks owned by Al Richards. (S. Holland)*

Back cover: *In 1986 the heavyweight hydraulic title was acquired by Mannesmann Demag Ltd. with their model 485 as supplied to Coal Contractors Ltd. for operation at their Roughcastle site in Scotland. It is seen here loading the first of the 130 tonne Cat 785 trucks that were imported into the U.K. At 552 tonnes, 2650hp and bucket capacities up to 30m its claim to the title was without doubt when upgraded to the following specification, 600 tonnes, 300hp and 33m capacity.*

About the Author:

Bill Huxley has a close affiliation to the subject matter of this book having worked with a wide range of plant and equipment over the past 25 years on numerous civil engineering and construction projects including opencast mining. It therefore comes as no surprise to find that one of his leisure interests is the history and operation of plant and equipment in the areas of agriculture, construction and civil engineering. Another of his interests being the products of Allis-Chalmers. He is a member of various preservation groups and is an active participant in the preservation scene. His previously published works include titles on Allis-Chalmers and Combines.

Introduction

Welcome to **'Opencast Coal — Plant & Equipment**, an informal illustrated review of mechanical development since its official inauguration in 1942, accompanied by short articles kindly contributed by long standing experts in the industry.

The compilation of this publication, conducted mainly in my leisure time, has proved at times an arduous but never-the-less most enjoyable task involving countless letters, phone conversations and numerous visits to London, Northumberland, Leicester, Mansfield, Merseyside, Yorkshire and elsewhere. It also has brought me into contact with a host of very informative, helpful, and interesting people whose combined efforts have made this book a reality.

Robert Moorhouse, with his typical Yorkshire determination and enthusiasm covered his area in great style; Billy Brinksman over the Pennines did likewise; Ian Hamilton, north of the border, contributed nicely and 'Digger' Lister rose to the occasion magnificently. To these and everyone mentioned throughout the pages, pleasant reading and many thanks!

Anyone with queries or wishing to comment on this publication, please feel free to do so to myself at the address below.

Bill Huxley
46 Loomer Road
Chesterton
Newcastle-under-Lyme
Staffs ST5 7LB

Acknowledgements

British Coal: Sue Bourne, Ivan Jameson, Dave Ketteridge and the Mansfield Staff; John Wilshaw, Chris, Stuart, Mac and the High Lane office; J.W.F. Hamilton and Steve Holland, Staffordshire House; David Openshaw, Southwest; Martin Thomas, Northern; T. Halliday, Brown Lees.
Others: D. Adams, A.D.A.S., T. Agnew, Artix Ltd., A.W.D. Ltd., Aveling Barford Machines PLC., Bucyrus Europe Ltd., D. Churchward, Clay Collieries Ltd., Construction News Publications, A. Cornes, P. Crosbie, E.C.C. International Ltd., Finnings Ltd., G. Hamilton, Barry Harvey, Red T. Higgins, R. Hooley, S. Howe, M. Hughes, Ironbridge Gorge Museum Trust, J. Kinchen, S. Johnson, J. Laing PLC., Liebherr GB Ltd., D. Lewis, A. Lister, H. Maguire, Marion (Dresser UK) Ltd., M.A.F.F., Ryan International Ltd., Crouch Mining, P. Merriman, Mannesman Demag Ltd., Miller Mining Ltd., G. Miller, P. Miller, Alfred McAlpine Plant Ltd., Sir R. McAlpine & Sons Ltd., Multidrive Ltd., Newcastle & Hanley Libraries, C. Nunn, H. Nunnick, O & K Ltd., Quarry Management, A. Rampling, Bert Ray, Radio Shropshire, R.B. (International) PLC., K. Roberts, P. Saint, Simba Machinery Ltd., J. Smith, Shropshire Star, B. Spencer, Bill & Clive Stone, Frankie Taylor, Taylor Woodrow Construction Ltd., J. Twinane, P. Thompson, A. Thorpe, R. Tindall, J.M. Trethewey, Vintage Roadscene Publications, V.M.E. UK Ltd., H. Webb, C.G. Weight, T. Wigsell, D. Wootton.

The Pioneer Years

Initiated in 1942 as a purely emergency measure to alleviate the shortfall in deep mined coal supplies, the industry owes its existence to the efforts of Albert Newby Braithwaite (later Major Braithwaite).

Being a director of the well established Sir Lindsay Parkinson & Co. Ltd. construction company and a Member of Parliament for Buckrose in Yorkshire, he was well placed to convince the Government of the viability of this means of recovering the much needed additional coal for assisting the war effort: coal that would otherwise have been unobtainable by deep mining methods.

The initial operations were under the control of the Mines Department of the Board of Trade who began to assemble a group of private contractors with whatever plant that was available for extracting coal from readily accessible sites. At this time, almost all the large excavators in the UK were owned by the iron ore, cement and clay industries which meant that the most readily available machines were of 2½ cubic yard capacity or less and the largest scrapers were the 12 yd. models suited to the Caterpillar D8 tractors.

Control of the industry soon passed to the newly created Ministry of Fuel & Power which then transferred the excavation and coal extraction activities to the newly formed Directorate of Opencast Coal Production operating under the control of the Ministry of Works which was headed by Major General K.C. Appleyard. He was later to be a member of a fact finding mission to the USA for the evaluation of the long established strip mining industry there, which operated large capacity walking draglines and high lift stripping shovels.

Thanks to the knowledge gained from the USA visit and a reciprocal visit in 1944 by a group of American experts, the 'Lease Lend' aid programme was to include a large quantity of heavy excavation equipment that would allow greater depths of coal to be recovered economically and efficiently. Bearing in mind the chaotic conditions of the time, the lack of expertise and the shortage of suitable equipment, it is commendable that a

Below: *Until the arrival of a detachment of Canadian Army engineers with a team of drilling experts and their Diamond drilling rigs who were seconded to operate on behalf of the Ministry of Fuel & Power and the Ministry of Works, hand operated rigs such as this were virtually all that was available in the opening stages of opencast operations. The situation improved in 1944 when, proprietary equipment as used in the long established U.S. strip mining industry began to arrive under the 'Lease Lend' scheme.*

Above: *Outcropping has been practised for a long time: possibly even since the time of the Roman occupation so, although outside the main theme of this book it is appropriate to feature this scene depicting the Apedale area in 1912. Since the late '40s this district has been worked by at least six different contractors with the current Crouch Mining contract for the extraction of 3.1m tonnes incorporating a comprehensive and final restoration and reclamation programme that will include the creation of the Apedale Country Park.*

total of approximately 23 million tons had been extracted by the end of 1945.

The cessation of hostilities released a considerable hotch-potch of plant; long forgotten names such as Osgood, General, N.C.H., Cletrac, Link Belt and Northwest were readily put to work alongside the more numerous Allis-Chalmers, Caterpillar and International Harvester models. Excavators included several hastily retrieved from such far flung locations as the Panama Canal zone, The Mississippi Levee undertaking and Alaska and included a 15 yd. Monighan as operated by Sir Robert McAlpine & Sons Ltd. in South Wales.

The most widely accepted method of excavation at that time was based on the use of long boom, large capacity draglines and Parkinsons, having gained considerable expertise with their large scale Wentworth group of sites in Yorkshire and Templenewsam near Leeds, set a pattern for future operations in 1949 when they commenced work with a second-hand Bucyrus-Erie 1150B of 25 yd. capacity at their Ewart Hill contract in Northumberland.

The industry was returned to the control of the Ministry of Fuel & Power between 1945 and 1952 when it became integrated with the National Coal Board and during that year it recorded its only deficit.

Additional large walking draglines, large excavators and other plant were imported in the 50s and, as UK manufacturers gradually returned to normal production, several new machines appeared including Fowler and Vickers tractors which, with the addition of the US designed machines built in satellite factories in the UK, gave the contractors the capability to undertake larger scale contracts.

Due to the continual increase in efficiency and capacity of equipment, the original total of seventy contractors had dwindled to a mere handful by the sixties but, with their hard earned expertise and the machinery to match, they had a far greater capability to undertake the larger, more complex contracts that were to become the norm rather than the exception.

Left: *With the turmoil of WWII and the fact that the few large capacity machines that were available operated in the ironstone and clay industries, anything that could function was pressed into service. This meant that a considerable number of inadequate machines such as Priestman, Ransomes & Rapiers, Ruston Bucyrus etc., many of which were of less than half cubic yard capacity, were the principal means of excavation in the opening months. Amongst the motley assortment of equipment were a number of steam shovels; these were often quoted as burning as much as they dug! This photo of a Ruston steamer came into my possession quite by accident: it fell out of a discarded parts book.*

Below: *Of the seventy or so contractors originally involved in opencast coal production, very few are active in the industry today. Most have either ceased trading, diversified into other activities or have been absorbed by competitors. A. Monk & Co. PLC were heavily engaged during the first twenty years and operated sites throughout North Wales, Lancashire and the Northeast which produced a total of 4,250,000 tons of coal involving 60,000,000 cubic yards of overburden removal and replacement. Some of the lesser known plant operated by them included a 1³/4 yd. Koehring walking dragline, a 3¹/2 yd Lima high lift shovel and Marion 6 yd. draglines. Along with other major contractors during the downturn in coal production in the '60s they became involved in the motorway programme and in specialised civil works.*

Above: *The Coalmoor Basalt Company of Little Wenlock, Shropshire, negotiated for, and operated the Malthouse site in 1942. The fact that the initial discussions were held with the Mines Department of the Board of Trade suggest that this would have been one of the earlier operations. Plant involved included a Ruston No. 6 steam shovel, a Ruston No. 4 universal excavator of 1/2 yd. capacity (which had cost £1,271 when purchased new on Jan 12th 1932), a 17RB, 24RB, Muir-Hill dumpers and the site runabout, an industrial Fordson tractor as seen with Mr. J. Banks, the driver, alongside. During my study of this area, I found evidence that opencasting had taken place prior to 1939.*

Right: *Major Albert Braithwaite's directorship of Sir Lindsay Parkinson & Co. Ltd. and his proposals to the House of Commons naturally involved his company from the opening stages of opencast coal production. Templenewsam, near Leeds, was one area but, the Wentworth group of sites were the most prominent ones of the time with a bank of five screening plants, each capable of handling 150 tons per hour giving an indication of the scale of the operation. Apart from the Monighan 'Walker' and the Canadian Dodge tipper, these 17RBs with skimmer equipment were quite popular for the removal of shallow level seams of coal.*

Left: *From the UK point of view, the rigid dump truck was originated by the Euclid Road Machinery Company, founded by George A. Armington in Euclid, Ohio, with a product range that included cranes, earth-moving equipment and locomotives. Their first purpose-built models, designed to replace the traditional rail car system in mines and quarries during the mid 30s, featured tyre tracks and were usually referred to as 'Trac-Truks' and had a 7 yd. capacity. This D-type is from 1935. The styling as we know it appeared in 1936 with the F-type and the famous Euclid Pioneer trade mark was also introduced at that time.*

Below left: *The Bucyrus-Erie Company of Milwaukee were noted for their range of walking draglines which incorporated designs from Oscar Martinson, an employee. Having purchased a controlling interest in the Ruston Hornsby company of Lincoln, England in 1930, they followed on with the acquisition of Monighan in 1931. From that time a considerable increase in production ensued, no doubt influenced by the considerable amount of work involved with the Mississippi Levee project. The range imported into the UK, many direct from the above mentioned operation varied from the 3W (cu yd) to the 15W as operated by Sir Robert McAlpine in South Wales. Fairbanks-Morse two-stroke diesels were the standard power unit but, at least one featured the Caterpillar engine used in the D8 tractor.*

Below: *This 8W, seen here at Hood Green, Barnsley, with an electric 100RB face shovel on bottoming up duties, was originally allocated to the Bath & Portland Stone Co. for work in Yorkshire during 1944 until it was transferred to Ruddock & Meighan Ltd. in 1947. Until opencast became an integral part of the NCB, control of the large equipment varied between the Ministry of Works and the Directorate of Opencast Coal Production section of the Ministry of Fuel & Power: all of which were covered by the Defence of the Realm act, which remained in force until 1958. Ruddock & Meighan were later absorbed by the P. Merriman company.*

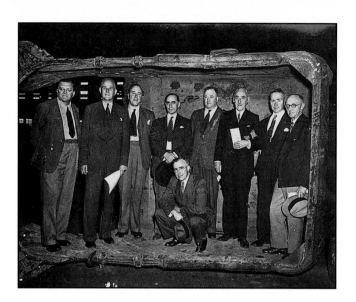

Left: *The group of men standing in this dragline bucket appear to be Americans: it is quite probable, therefore, that they would be members of the 1944 mission of strip mining experts to visit the UK to instruct on machinery utilisation and general site organisation. Also during this period, a group of government and construction industry officials visited the U.S. on a fact finding visit to numerous American operations that had long standing experience of coal extraction. Among the construction members were Mr. Arthur Monk and a member of the Sir Robert McAlpine family.*

Top right: *This Euclid R15 dumptruck in uncommon pose wa[s] photographed at the Strand site at Sidewood, Biddulph, North Staff[s] in the 50s. Mishaps, such as depicted here, are evidence of the fa[te] that can befall the unwar[y]*

Below: *Opencasting in Scotland commenced slightly later than in England with Whatlings Ltd. being one of the first to operate in 1946: an interesting aspect of their early work was the seven mile journey made by a 350 ton model 6W Monighan walking dragline from Bogside to Kelty during which it excavated its own crossings and a few power lines that happened to be in its way! The 6W appears to have been the most numerous size to be imported although 3 & 5Ws became products made by Ruston Bucyrus Ltd. Mirlees, National Gas and Petter diesels of the rail and marine type were ideal replacements for the original Fairbanks Morse engines.*

Below right: *'Lease Lend' and subsequent material aid programme[s] brought in a wide variety of equipment and vehicles both new an[d] second hand: amongst this mixture were Mack chain-drive dum[p] trucks as operated by Taylor Woodrow Construction Ltd. at the fir[st] Welsh contract at Pwll-Du and the subsequent Blaen Pig site. [A] 100RB is seen here undertaking the loading operation[s]*

Above: *The Euclid SS12/B series 13 yd. bottom dumps operated in conjunction with the BV loader. Initially introduced into the UK by Laing and Tarmac, they provided an almost continuous system of earthmoving in suitable conditions. 'A ton a second' was the bold claim of the time. The loader was virtually a giant plough combined with the elevating loader and hauled by a D8 until the appearance of the Allis Chalmers HD19 and 20s with torque convertor drive. The bottom dumps were GM or Cummins powered and featured a rear wheel activated winch for the door operation.*

Below: *The Euclid R15 (FD) truck was the mainstay of UK trucking operations for a long period, the company establishing their U.K. plant at Motherwell, Scotland. In 1950 this became the first U.K. product available with power units supplied by Cummins, GM, Leyland and Rolls Royce. This early, Cummins powered example was owned by the M.J. Gleeson company and is seen with Stan Helliwell in control. From 1953, the company became the Euclid Division of the General Motors Corporation (GM). The R15 was affectionately referred to as the '9-yarder' throughout the industry.*

Right: *By the early 50s several of the larger American manufacturers had established plants in the UK: Cletrac, for a while had a trading agreement with Blaw-Knox who also built construction equipment under their own name, P & H (Pauley & Harnischfeger) for a short period operated with Newton Chambers as NCH until Koehring arrived on the scene which then created the NCK range of excavators. Allis-Chalmers operated through the Mackay distributorship and Ransomes & Rapier Ltd., who had commenced production of walking draglines through an association with the Marion company in the late 30s were soon to be acquired by NCK. The 423 pictured here featured a good working but notoriously bad starting P6 engine, a fluid flywheel, poor traveling ability and was awfully noisy in operation. This machine was operated by John Croft on a Yorkshire DP in 1951 and he still has not recovered from the experience! Thankfully, the NCK 304 ³/₄ yd model rendered this less than pleasant to operate beast obsolete.*

Below: *The first of the four Bucyrus Erie 1150B walkers to arrive in the UK: this one purchased second-hand by Sir Lindsay Parkinson Ltd. for their Ewart Hill, Northumberland contract. Trouble arose in the beginning with the difference between the U.S. and UK electricity frequency but as a stop gap measure a five bank generator station with three in operation at any one time provided a solution until specialist electrical experts provided frequency changers or booster stations as the complete answer. With its 180 ft. boom and a bucket capacity of 22-25 yds. Parkinsons noticed an immediate and noticeable upturn in production figures.*

Left: *An early type of portable drilling rig was designed by General Appleyard and carried his name, it consisted of an horizontal auger type machine mounted on a truck chassis and would have proved useful on some sites. Another early design was the 27 RT Blast Hole Drill. This was track mounted with propulsion and drill operation by either diesel engine or electric motors and built by RB to a BE design. It was however, not until the mid 50s that any significant improvements occurred when the Joy 56 and 58s appeared with mechanical drive, hydraulic feed and air flush operation. Crouch preferred the Joy 58 models while Alfred McAlpine selected the Bucyrus 50R heavyweight with a 12 inch hole capacity for their Pool Covert site.*

Below: *New for 1953 were the Euclid 22 ton BITD 250HP Rolls Royce powered trucks that soon became a regular sight on most sites. In 1955 several were adapted as high capacity coal haulers by the replacement of the skips by bottom dump trailers built by the Eagle trailer company for operation on the Costain Acorn Bank site in Northumberland. These were used in conjunction with high speed Derricks to wind the coal out of the hole. Some of Euclid's earliest models had been articulated, with Ford trucks as the prime movers. Eagle also had some earlier experience with building some heavy duty side-dump quarry trailers attached to AEC units in 1949.*

Above: With material shortages lasting well after the cessation of hostilities, the regular auctions of ex military equipment were to play an important role in maintaining operations until such time as new machinery and vehicles became readily available. Such was the severity of the situation that numerous Sherman and other army tanks were converted for scraper operation while A-C, Cat, IH and other makes and types of plant were much sought after. Towed scrapers by Blaw-Knox, Garwood, Onions, RB/BE and Le Tourneau were also much in demand. The Cat D7 with 9 yd scraper and the D8, IH & 8R series with 12 yd 'Boxes' (scrapers) as seen here were in widespread use throughout the industry.

Right: Typical early backfill scene: an IH TD18 dozer with cable blade operated from the rear-mounted cable control unit (ccu), two of the large fleet of FD Euclids owned by the Wolverhampton-based Wilson Lovatt company and a Gallion grader built under license in this country by the British Jeffrey Diamond company of Wakefield, Yorkshire, who sold them under the Wakefield name. Neither these nor the contemporary Blaw Knox BK10 and BK12 models were to emulate the success of the Aveling-Austin or Caterpillar models. BJD, whose main interests lay with deep mine equipment are now controlled by Dresser Industries Inc. who, incidentally have merged their IH construction machinery interests with Komatsu of Japan.

Left: *Not to be outdone by the HD19 torque converter tractor, in 1947 IH unveiled their heavier, more powerful TD24. Still featuring their unique starting system, it also featured geared planetary steering that allowed dozing on the turn and it became quite popular here thanks to a substantial dealer network handled by J. C. Oliver (later R. Cripps & Co. Ltd.), Lumley Saville Ltd and James Bowen in Scotland. Well known users included Laing and Leveretts of Attleborough, Norfolk while the Lumley hire division also operated a large number. The later TD25s and 30s were overshadowed by the success of the Cat range but the medium size RR powered TD20 did become relatively popular. As with A-C, their motor scrapers were not heavily promoted in the UK.*

Below: *Carringtons Coppice, Derbyshire; the Laing flagship site of the late 40s. At 178 ft, it was the deepest site of the period, holder of a daily record of 4932 tons of coal produced. It was also the subject of cinema, BBC and press coverage, the scene for the film 'Moving Earth' with commentary by the renowned Freddie Grisewood and was visited by numerous overseas guests. When coaling ceased at 5pm on August 22nd, 1949, a total of 523,623 tons of coal has been extracted. Plant involved included this 37RB loading a 'Sweatbox' Ford 7V, V8 powered tipper, together with 2½ yd Ransomes & Rapier W90 and 5 yd W150 diesel powered walkers, two Rapier 490 draglines, a 490 shovel and 17RB, 19RB, NCK and Link-Belt coal shovels.*

Right: *Ransomes & Rapier widely advertised their W1800 dragline with its 40 yd. bucket as the largest machine available during a period of the 50s. Their brochures would not have included this bottom of the range diesel powered 2½ yd W90 in this location on the 29th May, 1954! D8s aided by a Lima 802 dragline had it back on firm ground by June 4th, not too badly damaged by its unscheduled excursion. Following the closure of the Ipswich works, Rapier and Bucyrus walking dragline and mining machinery interests are now handled by Bucyrus Europe Ltd.*

Below: *As well as the previously mentioned Kenfig Hill site in Glamorgan, Wilson Lovatt also operated the Terpentwys contract near Pontypool. The principal earthmovers here were two of the three 1150Bs purchased by the N.C.B. in 1953 and as with the Parkinson machine that was acquired, they were nearly ten years old when commissioned. The 'Oddball' of the fleet had General Electric componentry as opposed to Westinghouse with the others and a 200 ft. boom instead of the usual 180 ft. All featured Ward Leonard controls and their working weight of 1200 tons also represented their hourly output.*

Below: Euclid were early on the motor scraper scene with their first prototype tested in 1939; their preference being for the three axle configuration. Derek Crouch Contractors Ltd. operated three of the TS18 twin Cummins powered models on sites in Durham from 1955. It was not until 1958 when the two axle 'Overhung' TS24 design appeared that they began to conform to the traditional layout. The TS14 appeared in 1960 as an ideal, competitively priced machine for smaller contracts and a further innovation occurred with the three engine-tandem bowl configuration, followed by elevating models, high capacity coal versions and push-pull hitches.

Right: The Baldwin Lima Hamilton Company having achieved notable sales of their 3½ yd. 1201 shovels and draglines through their Jack Olding distributors, negotiated for its UK production with the North British Locomotive Company of Glasgow. The first three produced, with 80ft booms, Hendrix lightweight buckets and two stroke, four cylinder Crossley diesels were purchased by Sir Robert McAlpine & Sons Ltd. in 1954, this machine being delivered to their Tramways site, Swanick, Derbyshire. One of the McAlpine's 1201s operated in South Wales was powered by a Waukesha diesel and possibly due to age was reported as having the characteristics of a steam-powered model operating on low grade coal!

Below: With a long record of military vehicle and tank production Vickers decided to apply some of this technology towards civilian equipment production, the result being the appearance of the 180hp RR powered VR 180 high speed crawler tractor in 1952. Dowsett Engineering Construction were one of the most prolific users of these and the example shown was one of six operated on their Lumley, Chester-Le-Street site in 1954. In the later stages of production they were renamed as the Vigor and joined by a four cylinder, 140hp Vikon model. Design faults, no doubt brought about by their far too optimistic top speed of 9.73mph resulted in their demise in the early 60s. The last working units would have been from the considerable number released by the army who gradually replaced them with Caterpillars and Fowler Challenger 33s.

Left: *With the post-war vehicle manufacturers being encouraged to cater for the revenue earning export market, ex-government auctions were again a boon to contractors forced to operate out-dated vehicles. Bedford QLs and Austin K5 4x4 trucks proved ideal for many utility tasks and for more arduous roles ex RAF 6x6 AEC fuel bowsers found a new lease of life as tippers on coal haulage, with another popular choice being the Austin K6 6x4 gantry truck. The Perkins P6 diesel conversion aided by their double-drive made them an ideal lightweight vehicle for on/off site duties with Alfred McAlpine being one of a number of users. A local example gave yeoman service for Spencers Transport over a long period running from Douglas and Shand sites.*

Below: *Fowler were another company who attempted to break the U.S. monopoly of the crawler tractor market in the 50s. Their larger Challenger 3 and 4 models powered by Meadows or Leyland engines suffered from a lack of development and were only moderately successful. The later, D7 'Look-a-like', the Challenger 33 achieved a greater degree of success, albeit on less arduous duties for River Boards, Councils and military applications. These 4s operated for Monk on the Maidens Cross contract near Burnley, Lancashire in 1955. Long serving operator, Howard Nunninck, remembers several unusual items of plant in that area, one being a three axle, twin engined, Euclid: quite possibly an LLD 50-tonner. Another interesting muck-shifting operation involved a D9 with Hyster logging winch, an R15 Euclid with snatch block and a dredge for the removal of peat beds. Someone had obviously seen the old Fowler steam ploughing engines in action.*

Above right: *A rather dubious duo! Thorneycroft Mighty Antar and Big Ben designs were basically aimed at the Oilfield and military markets. This normal control layout would have been unsuitable for confined sites not to mention the driver discomfort. The Koehring/NCK Skooper loader based on the conventional 205 1/2 yd machine with hydraulic crowd and dump was definitely not one of the better known designs from this well known company.*

Below right: *Although opencast operates on a national basis, the North East was a particular strong hold for operations with, eight sites producing coal during the late forties and fifties. This 6W is shown crossing the Great North Road near Durham over a two foot sand carpet to protect the road surface and gas and water mains. Bill Stone, second from right on the pavement spent a long time with the company mainly involved with administration and tendering duties.*

Above: *1955 saw the introduction of two heavyweight dozers: Cat introduced the 315hp D9 while Euclid opted for a twin version of their C6 and marketed as the TC12, with almost 400hp, definitely the largest of the era. GM/Cummins powered, it was available with cable or hydraulic blade equipment, front mounted single drum winch or rear single and double drum options. The rear mounted radiator and fan assemblies gave them a distinctive look and allowed for the sleek frontal outline. It was later uprated to 440hp and slightly refined as the 82-80 series. Operators included Sir John Jackson Ltd. and Sir Robert McAlpine with the Blackwood Hodge dealership including them in their Euclid Wagon Hirers fleet.*

Below: *The Poplars, Cannock site operated by R.A. Davies (Midlands) Ltd. was the largest in the area in its time and would eventually field one of the largest fleets of machinery on UK sites. This 50s scene, showing the site in its early stages, features a Cat 2U with Birtley hydraulic blade, a two yard 43RB and one of its two Scammell Mountaineer Meadows powered trucks in operation. While very successful with their heavy haulage tractor units they did not fully come to terms with dump truck production for opencast operations. At a later stage Davies also operated a heavyweight bonneted Foden with a 450hp Rolls Royce turbocharged diesel, although subject to numerous modifications this also failed to make the grade.*

Below: *A 1956 view of the Dehli site in Northumberland operated by the Dowsett Engineering Construction Company. Although having official makers designation numbers Monighan machines were usually referred to by their cubic yard capacity. This makes the loading of 9 yd Euclid and Foden dump trucks by a 6 yd machine something of a mis-match but, the age of larger, evenly matched equipment was still some time away. Completing the picture are a trio of Ruston 27RT blast hole drills, a 19RB loading coal into a Bedford OY, 43 and 54RB face shovels, a Vickers VR180 dozer with overhead winch operated blade and ex RAF bowser trailer.*

Left: *Scammell 6x6 Constructors were useful for special applications such as drilling rig applications: this one, operated quite successfully around 1957 in the Wintersett area near Wakefield for Drilling and Prospecting International Ltd. As Robert Moorhouse remembers, in anything less than firm going, they did tend to leave clues as to their destination and were later superceded by the lighter, more sophisticated units mounted on County and similar style tractors.*

Below left: *In 1954, following the NCB purchase of the three Bucyrus-Erie 1150B draglines, two Marion model 7800s were supplied with 280 ft booms and 22 yd buckets for operation on the James Miller & Partners Radar South contract in Northumberland. Following the award of the £13.25m Radar North contract to Crouch in February '57, Marion no. 9997 was transferred up to the new site where, in due course a 240 ft boom and 30 yd bucket was fitted in place of the original equipment. No. 9998 later moved up also but, on the arrival of the 1550W in 1969 it was sold to a client in Canada, where it is thought to be still operational. H.S. (Digger) Lister at left with his removal team depicted during the move in April of that year.*

Below: *1958 was quite an important year for the opencast industry: the Defence of the Realm Act (DORA) was replaced by the Opencast Coal Act and a projected down-turn in coal requirements led to the closure of numerous smaller, less essential sites. This did not apply to the larger, longer running contracts in operation at Poplars, Acorn bank and Radar etc. This press photo would have been intended to highlight the Cat DW/PR 21 Athey Wagons in use here. Based on the successful DW21 scraper design introduced in 1951, they were relatively efficient although somewhat slow on gradients. Lima 2400 dragline and a six yd 150BE electric shovel operated with the 14 PR units on site. The D4 on clean-up would be an ex-ministry 2T or 7J model with 'Leaky' La Plante Choate hydraulics. The drivers of the Cat 112 grader and D8 at far right appear not to have seen the camera!*

Left: *By the 60s heavy haulage had become something of an industry in its own right with a long list of once famous names that have since mostly disappeared. Hallett-Silberman, Sunters of Northallerton, Muntons of Ruskington, McKeoghs and of course, Robert Wynn of Newport, better remembered for their long time use of Diamond T's and their Hall-Scott powered Pacific units. Probably the most prominent of the time were Pickfords with their considerable fleet of Scammell Constructors. The load shown here is a 1150B tub centre section from one of the two machines transferred from the completed Acorn Bank site of Costains to the nearby Crouch site at Radar during 1966.*

Below left: *Lunch break at Radar: the uncommon Smith 21 shovel, an example of which is seen here being serviced was noted for its cross pedal (left pedal to right lever) system. Gardner 6LW powered, it was a reliable machine but more widely used in quarry and plant hire activities. The popular AEC Mammoth Major 6 trucks, usually with 11.3 litre engines were widely used with Wimpey owning a considerable fleet including the later, rather heavy Park Royal cabbed versions. An air controlled 30RB coal shovel and Marion 111997 make up this 1958 scene.*

Below: *A late 50s arrival were the 15 & 18 yd AEC 'Dumptruk' models: developed by the Maudsley division of Associated Commercial Vehicles. They featured the AV 1100 turbocharged engine of 360+hp coupled to a three-speed transmission via a Twin Disc diesel torque system and had leaf spring suspension all round. Some were produced with side dump bodies and considerable development work was undertaken by the distributors Scottish Land Development Corporation at Poplars and other locations. This scene is of a trial unit working at Radar. Following the Leyland acquisition of ACV and its subsidiaries in 1962 production from the Thorneycroft plant (who had also built limited numbers of other dumptrucks) never seriously challenged AB, Euclid (Terex) or the soon to appear Cat 769A 35-tonners.*

Below: *Aveling Barford, having some pre-war experience of earthmoving machinery with their 4$^{1}/_{2}$ yd shuttle dumper resumed peace-time activities with an upgrading exercise that included adding a third axle and other modifications that resulted in a 9 yd truck (or over sized shuttle dumper) still featuring the twin steering wheel arrangement with reversible seat. Several were operated by Laing at Whitley Bay in the late 40s. This model was superceded by the four wheel 13-17-ton SL series, still more dumper than dumptruck. No doubt inspired by the success of the Euclid products they announced the successful 30-35-ton SN range in 1958. The twenty strong Davies fleet were predominately 400/450hp RR powered but a V12 GM option became available along with limited use of Dorman and other makes. Powershift or manual transmissions were optional and the rear suspension was classed as semi-rigid. Another very popular machine of the period was the Aveling-Austin 99H four wheel drive, four wheel steer grader license-built from the American Austin-Western Company since 1950.*

eft: *In the late 50s, the Poplars site operated at least four of the 60 Lima 2400s estimated to be at work in the UK. Rated at six yards for hovel duty and seven with a lightweight dragline equipment they were, along with the 150RB/BE, the optimum size for dragline use, both for e trucks available and the sites of the time. Ward Leonard controls, Cat D397 power units and 120 ft booms were the standard features of hese 200+ ton machines. Bearing in mind the rapid acceptance of hydraulic shovels and backhoes from the mid 70s and the use of larger npacity cable machines, a very creditable two dozen were still operational in the mid 80s.*

Below and inset: *Allis-Chalmers UK representation was through the Mackay Industrial Equipment distributorship based at Feltham, Middlesex; they did not handle the situation at all well. Only six of their quite effective 360 motor scrapers were imported, three to Hall of Morpeth and the others to the late Jim O'Sullivan, based quite near their HQ and a long standing A-C operator who operated them successfully for several years. When the spare parts situation became too acute he split them and adapted the bowls as towed scrapers for use with his 22A series D8s which had been the first products from the Caterpillar factory in Scotland in 1958. The engines from the O'Sullivan scrapers were eventually used as replacement units for some HD20 and 21 tractors that I had located still operational in East Anglia and which had been the better selling models from A-C. Sir Robert McAlpine & Sons Ltd. were quite probably the largest operators of HD21s, several of which eventually were sold to C.A. Blackwell Ltd.*

Left: While the 802, 1201 and 2400 Lima models were in wide spread use, their smaller construction site sizes were quite rare. These two coal shovels from their 24-44, ¹/₂-1 yard range operated by Ruddock & Meighan at Higham in 1959 would, I feel have been out priced by the 19/22RBs and similar UK built machines that were beginning to become more readily available.

Right: Prior to the considerable growth in road traffic during the sixties and the subsequent legal and environmental laws that followed it was quite normal to travel machines short distances by road. This Lima 2400, one of the Davies fleet at Poplars was required at their nearby Cheslyn Haye operation so, early one Sunday morning in the late fifties it clanked its way a short distance along the A5 and then via the A34 to its destination.

Below left: The Marion Power Shovel Company (now a member of the Dresser Industry Group) operated in the UK through their Babcock-Marion association which catered mainly for cranes and excavators for the construction industry. This 4¹/₂ yd 111M shovel is seen 'double spotting' a pair of 15 ton Euclid trucks in the ownership of Wilson Lovatt Ltd. A similar machine, operating as a dragline travelled under its own power through my village during the late 50s when in the ownership of R.A. Davies Ltd. When operating at night the howl of the twin 'Jimmies' could be heard over a large part of the city as comments to the local papers confirmed.

Below: The rigid frame rear-wheel steer 2 yd Cat 944A wheeled Traxcavator of 1959 was the first of their wheel loader range to appear. An important improvement on some of the other makes of the period was the forward mounting of the loader frame, this gave a greater safety factor and provided better access. Articulated models arrived on the scene from 1963 (Mathews Brothers patent) and by 1968 the range had grown to include the 10 yd 992 and from 1965 compaction modifications were available until the arrival of custom-built compactors and landfill models in the early 70s.

Left: Clark-Michigan, perhaps better known in the UK as manufacturers of transmissions and loading shovels introduced a number of their Wheeled Tractor dozers into this country. This Cummins 600hp V12 powered 480 Tractor dozer, on arrival at London docks was sold immediately to Davies for work at their Polesworth contract. Although basically intended for push loading duties for which it had a built-in pushing block, the hydraulic down pressure and 15 degree left or right tilt mode gave it the capability for solo operating. The 9 ft tyres would propel its 47-tons along at 28mph and, at £33,000 it was a very expensive but efficient method of loading scrapers quickly. When required, it worked on the nearby Poplars site.

Below left: The 60s may have been a period of restraint and uncertainty within the industry but, never-the-less, improvements in operational techniques and mechanisation continued as can be seen by the arrival of this Krupp Bucket Wheel Excavator (BWE) at Radar during 1961. Designed for excavating material such as this top lift of alluvial drift on a 40ft face, its continual output makes it, theoretically, the ultimate in earthmoving with an annual rated capacity of up to 2,000,000 yds. The 300-ton unit loaded a conveyor system of almost 5000 ft in length with the mobile spreader unit featuring a 98 ft boom of 28 ft discharge height. During its latter days in the early 70s, trucks replaced the spreader section.

Below: Following the completion of the Tirpentwys contract, 1150B no. 47858 moved up to the Poplars site while the other one made the short journey to the recently awarded Crouch Abercrave contract in 1964. An indication of the magnitude of the erection task can be seen by this scene involving derricks and truck mounted cranes. Also operated on this site were two 150RB electric shovels, a fleet of V12 Detroit (GM) powered Barford SNs and a Rapier W150 diesel powered walker. This was one of the essential contracts for Anthracite production and eventually produced almost 2,000,000 tons.

Left: Sir Alfred McAlpine & Sons Ltd., having gained considerable earthmoving experience with their numerous airfield construction contracts in the early 40s were ideally placed to engage in opencast operations. Their initial contracts involved the take over of several small existing sites in Lancashire during 1943. As was the situation of the time, plant was in short supply and the largest excavators that were available were the 802 Lima and the 2 yd 43RBs. A depot was established at Crows Nest near Wigan to handle plant repairs and overhauls for the wide assortment of well worn equipment which would eventually include converted Sherman tanks and a rare 44BE excavator.

Below left: McAlpine operated a considerable number of sites throughout Lancashire, north Wales and the Midlands with the Pool Covert, Wrexham contract being the largest at 2,5000,000 tons and involving 18,000,000 cu.m. of excavation during the period 1956-66. Among the vast assortment of plant involved was a 6W Monighan that had operated in Lancashire and a quite rare 200W Monighan that had been obtained in 1950. One interesting task for this machine was the lifting, transporting and positioning of the Bailey bridge that carried the coal transport over the A525 road to the screens. The truck fleet was a varied assortment of Euclid B1 & B2s, R15, 27, 35 & 45s, Barford SNs, Fodens and some of the first Cat 769As. These operated under an electric 110RB, a 100RB and a diesel electric 110RB. By 1964 RB had built 100 examples of this model. Bucyrus Europe Ltd. now handle the Bucyrus and Rapier ranges of mining machinery. During a most enjoyable informal discussion with the legendary muckshifter Des Diamond, long serving plant manager Don Dexter and the 'Ace of Engines' Bill Law, I understood the often quoted phrase "McAlpine's Fusileers", a lighthearted reference to the loyal band of followers associated with 'Macs'. Host Brian Fairclough, himself having given a lifetime service to the company joined in with the others in providing considerable interesting information of the company history. Don recalled numerous machines that were of an experimental nature and recalled the removal of RR engines from their Vickers tractors to upgrade the A-C HD20s.

Below: Ruston-Bucyrus Ltd., currently trading as RB (International) PLC., were the most prolific excavator manufacturers in the UK. at the time of the Bucyrus-Erie take over in 1930. The No. 4, 1/2 yd Universal excavator was their most popular model until U.S. designs were introduced: the 3/8 yd 10RB being an early example in the mid 30s with the 3W & 5W walkers appearing in 1939; these originating from the Monighan designs. Possibly the most widely used model in the 3/4 yd range was the 22RB introduced in the 50s. From the outset it proved to be a versatile, reliable rugged machine, so much so that, although updated through the years, the basic design remained unaltered and, by special order, is still available today. RB were a little slow in adopting air control operations but, following the successful introduction of the 30RB this system began to be phased in. The replacement for the 54RB appeared in the 60s with the 61 & 71RBs of 3-4 yd capacity full air control only. As a result of the sale of the Ruston Hornsby engine division to GEC, a variety of power units were offered with Cummins being a popular choice. The 71RB, eventually uprated to 4 1/2 yds became a widely used machine with many top contractors on medium sized sites until the early 80s.

Left: *In keeping with the other major UK manufacturers, RB simply just did not commit themselves to the rapidly emerging hydraulic market that was emerging in the 60s. I personally remember one of the first Hymac 480s on trial at Methyr Tydfil which gained rapid acceptance and by 1968 Hymac had progressed to the 1290 hydraulic shovel, probably the first to work as a coal shovel when demonstrated for Parkinson on a nearby site. Following the disastrous 3RB of 1963 which was a hydraulic backhoe unit mounted on a 10RB undercarriage, RB's next efforts were the 20H and 30H models: these featured Detroit diesels, U.S. low pressure hydraulics and a few other undesirable features but, a definite improvement. UK designed and built models appeared in the 70s but, by this time they, and the other major UK cable excavator manufacturers had missed the boat.*

Below left: *With the availability of countless derelict deep mine spoil tips another form of opencasting arose in the form of tip washing. One of the earliest operators was Ryan Plant Ltd. of Treforest, South Wales. Founded in 1947 by Mr. Larry Ryan following his release from the Canadian army, his first venture involved dredging the river Rhymney where, in February of that year he reclaimed 42,000 tons of fine coal using only a three quarter yd N.C.H. and a 10RB dragline. At the peak of operations the company owned what was probably the largest fleet of 22RBs in the UK along with a considerable fleet of Euclid C6s, Cat 22A and 68A D8 dozers and ancillary plant and road vehicles.*

Above and below: *A very much upmarket twin engined scraper appeared on the scene in 1963, this was the Cat 657 and with an eventual combined output of 950hp its 44 yd capacity created a new trend in high speed earthmoving, especially when push loaded by solo or dual rigged D9s. Following the sale of the first unit to the Western Excavating division of English China Clays Ltd. by Bowmakers (Finnings) Ltd. rapid acceptance arose with large fleets built up by Merrimans, Blackwells, Alfred McAlpine, MacGregor, Davies and Crouch etc. This example, one of three for Crouch is crossing the Tyne bridge en route to Radar in 1967.*

Above: *Twin powered scrapers such as this Euclid TS24 have a definite advantage over the single engined variety but, when faced with peat or other unstable material the dragline comes into its own. An expensive but sometimes unavoidable method or earthmoving it does avoid the necessity of bringing in alternative plant or vehicles for small quantities and both the scrapers and the 54RB can resume their normal activities when required. This scene is thought to involve a stocking ground area near Westfield, Scotland.*

Below: *For a considerable time during the 60s and 70s, the Cat D9G reigned supreme for heavy duty push loading and ripping applications: normal output was 385hp but, temporarily this one was zero rated! With the introduction of the 410hp D9H additional options included the 'side by side' dual tractor, three track layout, air/hydraulic steering and a 24 ft blade. The other ultra high output model was the D9H DD (duplex drive) tandem coupled, with sprung pusher blade and, again single operated.*

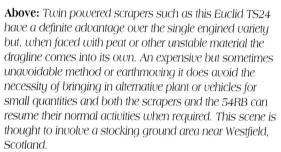

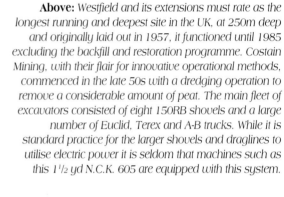

Above: *Westfield and its extensions must rate as the longest running and deepest site in the UK, at 250m deep and originally laid out in 1957, it functioned until 1985 excluding the backfill and restoration programme. Costain Mining, with their flair for innovative operational methods, commenced in the late 50s with a dredging operation to remove a considerable amount of peat. The main fleet of excavators consisted of eight 150RB shovels and a large number of Euclid, Terex and A-B trucks. While it is standard practice for the larger shovels and draglines to utilise electric power it is seldom that machines such as this 1½ yd N.C.K. 605 are equipped with this system.*

Above centre: *The 'Glorious 12th' in August 1969 had an added attraction in Northumberland: it was the day that the 65 yd 1550W dragline dug its first bucket-full for Crouch at Radar. Soon christened 'Big Geordie' this largest land-based dragline in Europe became something of a celebrity. Featured in the 1973 Guinness Book of Records, the subject of films and TV, gazed upon by countless visitors of all ages from far and wide, it was later to participate in its own 'Marathon'. Some vital statistics include a boom length of 265 ft, working weight of 2857 tons, digging depth of 150 ft, dump reach of 233 ft, a power input of 13650hp and a production rate of 2600 yds per hour.*

Left: *One of the longest running sites was the Wimpey Maesgwyn Gap contract scheduled to produce a total of 11,000,000 tons of Anthracite. Prime mover on this site was the Ransomes & Rapier W1800 dragline which commenced work in March 1961. With a 247 ft boom and an Esco 40 yd bucket weighing 33 tons with fittings the heavyweight title for this type of machine had been held with previous similar machines supplied to the Ironstone industry. It worked continually until 1975 when it underwent a full refit prior to recommencing work on an adjacent twelve year contract. Operated on a seven day, three shift pattern its working cycle on a 70 ft dig and ninety degree dump was sixty four seconds giving it a 1750 tons hourly output, again equaling its own weight. Following the completion of the contract it was sold to the U.S.A.*

The Modern Times

In the late 1960s the mainstays of the earth-moving equipment in the UK were crawler draglines and rope shovels such as the Lima 2400, Manitowoc 4600 and Bucyrus 150RB together with associated fleets of 35-50 ton dumptrucks of which Aveling Barford and Terex had large shares.

A few large electric walking draglines were in operation: four 19/20 cu.m. (25/27 cu.yd.) Bucyrus 1150Bs which had been purchased second hand from the USA in the early 1950s, a 23 cu.m. (30 cu.yd.) Marion 7800 built in 1955 and a Rapier W1800 manufactured in the UK which commenced work in March 1961 as the then largest dragline in the world with a 31 cu.m. (40 cu.yd.) bucket on a 5m. (247ft.) boom. It was to be 1969 before this machine was exceeded in size in the UK when "Big Geordie", the 50 cu.m. (65 cu.yd.) Bucyrus 1550W went to work.

The early 1970s heralded the introduction into the UK of the 6 cu.m. (7.8 cu.yd.) O&K RH60, the first of the 100 ton plus size of hydraulic excavators which were to steadily grow in size and numbers and would eventually oust the rope machines as the industry's main prime movers.

Other large hydraulic excavators introduced in the same decade included the Poclain EC1000 and 1000 CK, the O&K RH75 and the Demag Hill. The first electric drive dumptrucks were introduced to the industry when eighteen Lectra Haul M100s were imported from the USA between 1970 and 1973.

However, rope machines remained in large numbers for many years and grew in size to around 8-9 cu.m. (10-12 cu.yd.) as site depths and overburden ratios increased. These conditioned also led to a requirement for larger draglines designed to be capable of being assembled and re-located quickly between relatively short life sites. These were introduced in the late 1970s by British Coal Opencast (BCO) in the form of three 9 cu.m. (12 cu.yd.) Bucyrus 380Ws and one 11.5 cu.m. (15 cu.yd.) Manitowoc 6400. Two 10 cu.m. (13 cu.yd.) Rapier W700s were subsequently purchased by NSM although

Below: *By the late 60s, coal production had fell to approximately 6.5m tons, its lowest ever: the four largest contractors involved Costain, Crouch, Parkinson and Wimpey continued operating along with a number of smaller operators. Due to the sheer magnitude of the contract further reference to the 'Deepest Hole in Europe' (Westfield) is justified. It had a vast screening and washery complex with NCB owned Sentinel shunting locos, and a vast array of plant including a German built conveyor system to transport the spoil from the crusher a distance of 3km to a 30m cu m dump. This layout with a designed 3440 tph output crossed a stream, two roads, a railway and terminated at this moveable spreader unit.*

Left: *Clark-Michigan added to their range of self loading, elevating scrapers (Hancock), wheel loaders and dozers with a batch of the T65 (ton) trucks with 700hp Cummins V112 or GM V16-671 series engines. Several units went on trial with Costain, Crouch and Wimpey as seen with this example being loaded by a 1950s designed Bucyrus-Erie 8 yd 190B. However, after detailed appraisal series production was not undertaken for a variety of reasons; one being a possible clash of interests with their transmission division. The complete batch were consequently transferred to a major Mediterranean construction project.*

these and the 6400 have now been sold to the USA.

Under optimum conditions, the most economical method of overburden removal is by the use of large walking draglines and in the mid 1970s, BCO began to replace its ageing machines with eventually four Bucyrus 1260Ws and two Rapier W2000 draglines with bucket sizes of 23-27.5 cu.m. (30-36 cu.yd.). BCO also continued to purchase 8-9 cu.m. (10-12 cu.yd.) rope shovels such as Bucyrus 195 RB, Marion 182M and P&H 1900 AL to meet the continuing need for machines of this size.

In 1980, the then world's largest hydraulic excavator, the 22 cu.m. (29 cu.yd.) O&K RH300 was introduced together with Wabco 170 ton electric drive trucks, and the 14 cu.m. (18.3 cu.yd.) Demag H241 appeared in the same year. These were followed by the 10 cu.m. (13 cu.yd.) Liebherr R991 in 1982, the 13 cu.m. (18 cu.yd.) O&K RH120 in 1984, and in 1986, the 14 cu.m. (19.6 cu.yd.) Liebherr R994 and the Demag H485 which is now the world's largest at 23 cu.m. (30 cu.yd.). Following its launch at Bauma 89, the 20 cu.m. (23 cu.yd.) O&K RH200 was introduced in 1989. The first 10.3 cu.m. (13.5 cu.yd.) Hitachi EX1800 was introduced in 1990 and the 18 cu.m. (23.5 cu.yd.) EX3500 went to work at the end of 1991.

The continued growth in size and population of the hydraulic excavator resulted in a corresponding increase in the size of dumptrucks and the ever popular Terex R50 began to be steadily replaced by the 85 ton size, the most common being the Caterpillar 777. This trend has continued with the introduction of significant numbers of Cat 785 (135 ton) and Cat 789 (170 ton) trucks.

Left and below: *The face loading ability of the Cat 992 loader with a 10 yd bucket and 600+hp gave a greater flexibility to site operations in certain applications. Continual improvements included tyre chains for operating in abrasive conditions, a high lift arrangement and a logging attachment. With the eventual arrival of the 992C version, 690hp and a 13.5 yd bucket were standard. These illustrations feature a bucket cleanout by a once ubiquitous 1 yd BTD6 Drott and loading an R65 Terex, both scenes being on the Crouch Llanilid contract in the Swansea valley in 1970. During that year Crouch produced 1,530,607 tons in Northumberland, almost a quarter of the overall total of 6.3m tons of coal from all UK sites.*

Right: *The acquisition of the Ruddock & Meighan company brought Merriman Ltd. into opencasting on a direct basis, although with their considerable fleet of 631 and 657 scrapers and long standing expertise they continued to undertake sub-contract earthmoving with Crouch being a major customer. This ex WD Douglas/AEC Militant truck-based Coles crane was their fitters muscle power on their Llanilid overburden contract. Having been employed on hire to this company in the past I can vouch for the speed and efficiency with which they handled their work.*

Below: *The upward trend in operating capacity continues: the first four of a total of fifteen 990hp Cat powered electric wheel drive trucks to be imported arrived at Llanilid. Badged as M85s they were actually to a higher specification and were given a 100 ton/67 yd rating. To match the increased truck capacity, Crouch operated this 182M high lift Marion shovel at Radar where another four of the M85s were assigned to operate. The Llanilid contract included one of three Marion 191M (10.7m), 363 ton shovels originally programmed for the since deferred Butterwell contract.*

Above: *Murphy Brothers undertook the long delayed Park Farm site contract in Goldenhill, Stoke on Trent during the early 70s. This site differed from most others in that a conveniently adjacent rail system handled the total output of coal produced here. Apart from the 120RB (which, being electric, was regularly vandalised prior to becoming operational) a considerable fleet of TS24s, Cat 631 & 657 and Wabco scrapers were involved along with a large fleet of Euclid trucks, Cat 769As and excavators including 22, 38, 54 and 150RBs together with two 2400 Lima's.*

Below: *Crouch replaced their fleet of site restricted AEC 690 trucks with a fleet of 24 Foden S80 on/off highway 24-26 ton Neville bodied, six wheelers. A mixture of 150 and 180 Gardners coupled to the Foden three range, 12-speed box with low ratio diffs gave satisfactory gradability performance. One bucketful from Big Geordie's 100 ton capacity bucket would be sufficient for at least six of these trucks at the road legal limit, a clear indication of its capability!*

Below right: *A radical departure from the time honoured rope shovel and dragline method of operating took effect with the introduction of the first 100 ton plus hydraulic shovels by Northern Strip Mining Ltd. for their Acretair site in north Wales during 1971. The greater mobility and digging power from this 6m capacity RH60 would soon take over the traditional 150RB/2400 share of the market and, with the subsequent introduction of the 7.5m RH75, an even greater impact was made. The first 75 entered service with Taylor Woodrow at Butterwell in 1976.*

Below: *From 1970 Aveling-Barford introduced the Centaur range of forward control trucks, initially with the 25 and 40 models. Considerable updating of the suspensions, Cat, Cummins and GM power options and the larger capacity resulted in considerable orders from Costain, Shephard Hill, Wimpey and Parkinson (latterly Fairclough-Parkinson). This later version is seen being loaded by an over matched Marion 191M in Wales, another of the pre-ordered Butterwell trio. Recent changes of ownership and the failure to enter the 85-100 ton sector has resulted in Aveling Barford losing ground on the opencast scene but, they do maintain a healthy share of the quarry and export markets.*

45

Left: *The next heavyweight hydraulic machine to arrive after the RH60 was the Poclain EC1000, ordered by Miller Mining for their Pithouse, Yorkshire site. Powered by three GM Detroit diesels it had a backhoe capacity of only 5½ yds as opposed to a range of 5½-10 yd buckets for the shovel version. Very few of these or the 1000CK replacement were imported, Shand Mining and Norwest-Holst being the only other users. Noise and a certain hydraulic problem could well have stunted sales and, when Demag introduced the H111 and H241 series from the late 70s, Poclain production was concentrated on their smaller, more popular models.*

Below: *August 23rd 1971, The Manitowoc Engineering Company shipped one of their model 4600 draglines from Milwaukee via M.S. 'Nordcap' to their UK distributor Messrs A. Long & Co. Ltd. of London. Its eventual destination was the Knackshaven, Co. Durham site operated by Ruddock & Meighan Ltd. Machine no. 46227 was equipped with the Cat D-379 power unit option (single and twin Cummins and Detroit Diesels options also available) and variable independent control (Vicon), 120-160 ft boom lengths and a capacity of 5-7m placed these slightly above the Lima 2400 and 150RB range. It has since operated under the Merriman-Meighan name.*

Above: *Koehring enter the hydraulic market again with a single unit of the 1266, twin GM powered 8 yd backhoe. This was taken on by Lehane Mackenzie & Shand Ltd. and operated in Wales until 1981 when it appeared in the 'for sale' column of a well known trade magazine. From an informed source I understand that it was not an outstanding success. Their rope operated models, particularly cranes, are highly regarded but they definitely neglected this market.*

Below: *RH60 'double spotting' a pair of Euclid R50s: these were products of the reformed company that evolved from the 1968 White acquisition of the Euclid trade name and certain U.S. plants. White trucks were absorbed by the Daimler-Benz company around 1977 and by 1985 had become a member of the Volvo-Michigan-Euclid (V.M.E) group.*

Right: *From 1958 AEC had produced an off road, half cab version of the Mammoth Major 6 which entailed a 10 yd dump truck body and super single rear wheels and tyres, it became very popular with many opencast and muckshifting operators. The Midex plant hire division operated by Davies from Woodville had probably the largest fleet in the UK with approximately 53 units, a small number of which featured conventional twin rear wheels which eased the half shaft problem in sticky conditions. From 1964 the model was upgraded into the bonneted 690 series with the AV691 200hp engine. Due to the constant acquisitions and 'rationalisation' programme of Leyland during the 60s and after, production moved to Aveling Barford and then Scammell and were badged accordingly. This Edbro coal bodied example was operated by Merriman-Meighan Ltd.*

Below: *The night of May 1st 1973 would have been a sleepless one for the residents of Widdrington village, Big Geordie goes 'walkies'. It is seen here crossing the A1068, its 56 ft by 10 ft shoes gave it a walking speed of 0.16mph on its journey to the adjacent Sisters site where it remained until it took the now famous walk widely known as 'Destination Butterwell' in 1977. It worked continuously on the Taylor Woodrow contract until the recent cessation of coaling there. It is currently awaiting a new home — can anyone help the old lady out?*

Right: *Owing to its sheer size and weight (2857 tons) the relocation of 'Big Geordie' from the Crouch 'Sisters' site to the recently awarded contract at Butterwell for Taylor Woodrow Ltd created a considerable amount of media attention. This article from a Crouch house magazine in 1977 well illustrates the enormity of the task and the manner in which it was accomplished.*

Walkabout' Spectacular

GEORDIE RRIVES DAY EARLY

 from the Contractors Company, led by Mr. gger' Lister, Director in charge of Opencast Mining, ccessfully taken 'Big Geordie' on a 2.6 mile walk ters Site at Widdrington to the new opencast coal ite at Butterwell, where the dragline will work for the years. The spectacular walk was the culmination of planning by Crouch staff in conjuction with s from the N.C.B. Opencast Executive based at , the North East Electricity Board, British Rail, the e North East Water Authority and Northumberland Council.

ordie' — accompanied by a small army of press men and crews — crossed three roads, the main London-Edinburgh he and a river and arrived a day early. To ensure a trouble

 Eastern Electricity Board engineers had to temporarily e a 66kV power line;
sh Rail engineers had to remove railway lines at Stobswood ng and lay a three foot thick carpet of shale across the

ch men had to bridge the River Lyne and each road with h ramp.

k was timed to cause the least disruption and it took 19 days e largest walking dragline in Europe was safely at Butterwell. ordie' covered 8ft 6ins at each stride and clocked up a steady on a closely surveyed cross-country route. The only hitch in the e came as the dragline began to cross the River Lyne. The huge long and 10ft wide — hit ground on the river bank and the ad to be manoeuvred onto a sounder surface. A power cable 'Big Geordie's' electric motors ran more than a mile from Sisters half of the journey and it was then transferred to the Butterwell the remainder of the journey.

When the walk was over, Mr. 'Digger' Lister paid tribute to the men who had helped to move 'Big Geordie'.

"It was a magnificent team effort," he told The Journal. "There were one or two occasions during the walk when naturally, we had problems to sort out in a hurry. The response from the men involved was tremendous. When we needed maximum effort, we got it. I don't think that any team could have given more.

"When you move a big machine like 'Big Geordie' you need people with the skills and the enthusiasm to be able to do it. We've got the best team in the business. They were marvellous".

The 'Big Geordie' drivers involved in the walk were Ronnie Vickers and Robert Hattell. The dragline is now working at Butterwell accompanied by Ronnie Vickers and Con Boyle.

TIP TOE ACROSS THE RAIL LINE

BIG Geordie noses its way slowly over the main London-Edinburgh railway line.

In the foreground, arms outstretched, an engineer keeps it on course . . . or could he be directing the traffic?
● Picture — British Rail Eastern Region.

Company thanks the engineers involved

THE Contractors Company would like to put on record their thanks to the engineers of the N.C.B. Opencast Executive, the North East Electricity Board, British Rail, the GPO, the North East Water Authority, and Northumberland County Council for their wholehearted co-operation in helping to get the dragline to Butterwell.

Said Chris Raine: "The spirit of co-operation between the various authorities was superb. We want them to know that we appreciate all they did to help us."

Team leaders controlled Geordie walk

ch personnel involved in the walk are pictured with one of the e huge dragline. 'Big Geordie' arrived at Butterwell a day he men involved in this achievement were:
 (left to right): R. Vickers, W. Telfer, C. Jones, T. Stokoe, P. MacDonald, J. Fisher, M. Hickey, M. Durham, H. Dane,

W. Curry, C. Robson.
Bottom row (left to right): A. Bell, G. Ashton, H. S. Lister, D. Heckles, G. Brotherson, J. Angus, P. Falconer, E. Wild, L. Atkinson, C. Raine, L. M. Ling.

THE Crouch team leaders on the 'Big Geordie' walk, working with Mr. H. S. Lister, who controlled the operation, were:

PETER Falconer (Senior Planning Engineer) who was in charge of the walk and the pre-walk civil engineering. He lives at Whitley Bay and has been with the company for 13 years.

CHRIS Raine (Planning Engineer) who assisted Mr. Falconer. He lives at Blyth and has been with the company for seven years.

GEORGE Ashton (Plant Manager) who was in charge of all mechanical and structural aspects of the dragline. He has been with the company for 20 years and lives at Stannington, Morpeth.

ALF Bell (Electrical Engineer) who was in charge of all electrical work on 'Big Geordie' and the associated electrical installations. He lives at Morpeth and has been with the company for 20 years.

RONNIE Vickers (Big Geordie Driver). Ronnie has 20 years service with the company, and lives in Newcastle-upon-Tyne.

ROBERT Hattell ('Big Geordie' Driver). He has been 7 years with the Company and lives at Lynemouth.

BILL Telfer (Foreman-civil engineering and roadworks). Bill was involved in the advance preparation of the walk-way for 'Big Geordie', and also the crossing of the river and roads. He lives at Widdrington, Morpeth, and has been with the company for 13 years.

JACK Angus (Chargehand-cables). Jack was in charge of the movement of the power cable for the dragline. He has been with the company for 20 years and lives at Morpeth.

Mr. H. S. 'Digger' Lister: "It was a magnificent team effort."

JOE Fisher (Bankman). Joe was in charge of directing 'Big Geordie' from the ground while the dragline was on the move. He lives at Felton and has been with the company for 15 years.

PAUL Final (Banksman). Paul, who has been with the company for three years, was also in charge of directing 'Big Geordie' while the machine was on the move. He lives at Stobswood, Morpeth.

Shucks! What happened to the injuns?

er and his crew who handled the civil engineering and s for the 'Big Geordie' walk are 'riding tall in the ese days. A film crew from NCB made sure of that. w, who filmed the walk in detail, found that almost re they went, there was an army of Crouch person-' over the crest of every hill with 'Big Geordie' close t was almost like a western cattle drive. After finding

Bill Telfer and his men at every major crossing of road, rail and river, members of the NCB crew decided to call the squad 'John Wayne and the round-up gang'.

The punch line came when 'Big Geordie' crossed the River Lyne. Said one spectator: "I see John Wayne and his gang are here again. Any minute now the injuns will attack!"

ew dragline swings into action — see back page

Left: *On March 26th 1980 the MV 'Terzie' sailed from the U.S. with a Manitowoc 6400 on board: this was allocated to Shephard Hill for operation in Cumbria. Its twin power layout was different in that a Cummins 450hp engine was located in a module on the truck frame while the other, a V16, 1600hp Cummins powered the upperworks from the conventional mounting place. Independent hydraulic track motor drive, 160ft boom, 15 yd bucket and their patented variable independent control system (Vicon) are the main features. British Coal Opencast have since sold this machine back to the U.S.A.*

Below: *Commencing in 1976, the first of five P&H 1900AL electric mining shovels arrive in the UK. With a capacity of up to 12 yds and an operating weight of 400 tonnes plus — of which 50 tonnes was counterweight ballast. They featured high position cabs to correspond with the increasing use of larger trucks. Two were to be NCB owned with the others purchased direct by Taylor Woodrow, Fairclough Parkinson and Wimpey Mining. During 1980 P&H also introduced five of their recently announced model 1200 hydraulic shovels of 183 tonnes and 10m capacity all of which were destined for W.J. Simms Sons & Cooke Ltd. (C.P. Holdings Ltd.). This scene is at the Taylor Woodrow, Chester House, Northumberland site where the fleet of 777A trucks are also loaded by an O&K RH120C and a 195RB shovel.*

Above: *The 80s was the era of the hydraulic excavator: O&K set the pace with their 500 ton, 23m RH300, the largest machine of its type at that time. To keep pace with its prodigious output, a team of 170 ton capacity, electric wheel drive, Wabco trucks were introduced. Following an initial spell at Swadlincote it was moved up to the Godkin, Heanor site in 1981 and remained there for the remainder of the decade. These Derbyshire schoolchildren find an appropriate name for it! Although only three were produced they would have provided considerable feedback for assistance in later designs.*

Below: *With the arrival of the Wabco's, some heavy duty haul road maintenance was called for. The answer to this problem was the 40 ton, 343HP Cummins powered O&K G350 grader with a 19 ft. blade and heavy duty 7 shank ripper. Having acquired the Faun heavy truck manufacturer, O&K brought over some 85 ton trucks for evaluation but no serious consideration appears to have been given to full scale introduction of these although their later articulated trucks are in current use.*

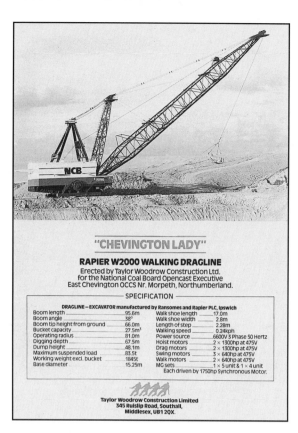

"CHEVINGTON LADY"

RAPIER W2000 WALKING DRAGLINE

Erected by Taylor Woodrow Construction Ltd.
for the National Coal Board Opencast Executive
East Chevington OCCS Nr. Morpeth, Northumberland.

─ SPECIFICATION ─

DRAGLINE – EXCAVATOR manufactured by Ransomes and Rapier PLC, Ipswich

Boom length	95.6m	Walk shoe length	17.0m
Boom angle	38°	Walk shoe width	2.8m
Boom tip height from ground	66.0m	Length of step	2.28m
Bucket capacity	27.5m³	Walking speed	0.24kph
Operating radius	81.0m	Power source	6600V 3 Phase 50 Hertz
Digging depth	67.5m	Hoist motors	2 × 1300hp at 475V
Dump height	48.1m	Drag motors	2 × 1300hp at 475V
Maximum suspended load	83.5t	Swing motors	3 × 640hp at 475V
Working weight excl. bucket	1845t	Walk motors	2 × 640hp at 475V
Base diameter	15.25m	MG sets	1 × 5 unit & 1 × 4 unit
		Each driven by 1750hp Synchronous Motor.	

Taylor Woodrow Construction Limited
345 Ruislip Road, Southall,
Middlesex, UB1 2QX.

Left: *Bearing in mind the total number of assorted makes and sizes of walking draglines operated in Northumberland since opencasting commenced it is not surprising that it has earned the title of 'Dragline County'! This commemorative poster announced the arrival of yet another latter day 'Giant of Bedlington' type of machine, this title had been bestowed on the original Parkinson owned 1150B in 1949. The erection contract, awarded in September 1982 involved a 52 week, £750,000+, computerised programme that produced some impressive statistics. In excess of four tonnes of 1mm welding wire and 2.9 tonnes of electrodes were used by the sixteen coded welders, a part of the total of thirty six personnel involved. The transportation required a total of 73 road vehicles and several cranes of up to 110 tonne capacity were in operation, also each joint in the gas filled boom was visually and radiographically checked to ensure that defect free welds were obtained. This 1845 tonne, 27.5m machine operated by Crouch Mining and the one operated by Miller Mining (currently awaiting site continuation at St. Aidans, Yorkshire) are the only examples in the UK.*

Below: *Euclid suffered from the lack of a strong dealer network for their 32-190 ton range of trucks. The R50s sold in reasonable numbers as did some other sizes but the R100 as seen on test at Butterwell did not achieve a notable market share. A.F. Budge (Plant) Ltd. operated three at their Kingswood, Cannock site but these were soon traded in for a fleet of R50s that were allocated to the Bateswood site and Cat 777 replacements went to Kingswood. V12 Cummins or GMs both of 1050HP were the power options, both operating through an Allison power shift transmission.*

Above: *Another new machine to appear on the UK opencast scene was the P.W.H. Wesserhutte SW 530 dragline purchased by French Kier Mining Ltd. in 1982 for their Kiersbeath site in Scotland. Cat powered and with a mixture of hydraulic and mechanical functions it arrived at the time when all hydraulic machines were gaining acceptance, resulting in the gradual demise of medium sized rope operated excavators. With a capacity of 7-8 yds it was competing with the Lima 2400B of which there were a considerable number still available in the UK. The company has since been sold to a private buyer with O&K (Orenstein & Koppel AG) acquiring the remainder of the group. Further mergers with German manufacturers are pending.*

Below: *High speed muck-shifting by Merriman-Meighan Ltd. on a Crouch overburden subcontract at Acklington Northumberland in the early 80s: the 30 yd. 631 scrapers have long been the top single engine model in the UK, usually push loaded by a single tractor but, when conditions demand tandem D9Gs with sprung blades provide sufficient muscle. Merriman owned one of the largest fleets of 657 scrapers during the 60s and, in fact provided the D9 pusher for the initial 657 serial no. 4D7046 that commenced work for the Western Excavating Company Ltd (ECC) on 29th November 1963. Charlie Green, the D9 driver for Merriman on that occasion currently operates his own plant hire company with several machines on opencast and washery work in the Midlands.*

Left: *The Coalfields Farm contract at Ibstock, awarded to Merriman Meighan Ltd. in 1976 and the Coalfields North extension awarded to Shand Mining in 1983 have only recently ceased coaling with a combined total of 14m. tonnes of coal produced. As well as the previously mentioned AECs, coal transport included eight Dutch built Terberg 8x8 heavy duty tippers that featured the F12 engine and other components from Volvo and which ran with loads well in excess of 30 tonnes; five Magirus Deutz 6x6 bonneted tippers and the veteran Fodens from the original contract. In action to the last, these were 310HP, semi automatics with the half cab design that was widely used on truck mixers of the period. Also involved were Big John and Little John, two of the four 1260W 24.5m. draglines obtained by the NCB from 1976 onwards.*

Below left: *The radically new design of the 1977 Cat D10 with elevated sprocket arrangement was evolved for several reasons including reduced sprocket wear and power train loading. At 700HP and an operating weight in the order of 75 tons it became the largest tractor available. Two of the first machines to operate here were owned by Stokey Plant Ltd. with others operated by large quarry owners. This scene was at the Crouch, Cadgerhall contract in Scotland in 1981. At this time a traveling 'Circus' demonstration took place with the stars involved comprising a Komatsu 455, a Fiat Allis HD41B and a D10.*

Above: *The Terex Corporation, having been sold to the now defunct IBH group in Germany were partially returned to GM ownership until a recent demerger saw the creation of a privately owned group that also embraces the Northwest Engineering Company, the Unit Rig Co. and the Detroit Diesel Corporation — all US based companies. At present the largest truck available in the UK is their 3311E of 85 tonne capacity but, with the Unit Rig range of mechanical and electric drive trucks extending to 240 tonnes capacity, there is a possibility that larger models may appear over here. Detroit Diesel have recently relinquished their total commitment to their long standing range of two stroke diesels by announcing a range of electronically controlled four stroke engines of 285-450HP.*

Left: *The Allis-Chalmers HD41B had first appeared at the Chicago Roadshow in 1963: powered by two of their 2100 series engines it was the largest machine of the time. A delay in production occurred until 1969 when it arrived on the market now powered by the V12, 524HP Cummins. The first to operate in the UK was obtained second hand by Whites of Froxfield, the Wiltshire based contractor and private site operators. On Jan 1st 1974, the Fiat and A-C construction machinery interests merged to create FiatAllis, the only immediate noticeable difference being the new blue/grey livery. Seen here is a later model HD41B with a Kelly ripper.*

Left: *Having sold the DJB truck range to Caterpillar, Mr. David J. Brown acquired the production rights and the Dunstable plant of the recently terminated Bedford truck division of Vauxhall Motors (GM). With the Bedford name being retained for the range of light vans built by Vauxhall. The long standing AWD title was brought back into use for the new range of trucks announced by the new owners. Perkins replaced the Bedford engines for the lighter models while the 425HP Cat 3406B was fitted to the new TM 40 of up to 25 tonnes payload for on/off site operation.*

Right: *Thirty eight years on, Marion 7800 no. 9997 with 240ft. boom and 30yd. bucket is still operational at the Taylor Woodrow Chester House site in Northumberland. On the conclusion of the contract in 1994 the 40th birthday present for this old timer will quite probably be the 'Hot Spanner'. Marion have supplied several types and sizes of machines to the iron ore and coal industries including 111M, 182M, 191M and 195M shovels and draglines and 7400 and 7500 walking draglines. With several other older walking draglines currently out of action, including 'Big Geordie' it would be nice to see one being retained as a momento of our industrial heritage but, owing to their size and the cost and location problems it would require some heavyweight sponsorship to achieve this aim.*

Below: *The David John Brown company introduced their DJB range of articulated dump trucks in 1974 featuring Caterpillar engines and running gear. With a high content of Caterpillar components it was understandable that these would be distributed through the Cat dealer network until, in 1986 they became wholly owned Caterpillar products. The original owners underwent a change of name to Artix Ltd and continued to supply the soon to be revamped range of trucks on a subcontract basis to Caterpillar. The 40 tonne capacity D400D seen being loaded by the popular, top of the range, 245B backhoe is on pre-delivery trial.*

Right: One of three Cat 215D LC backhoes operated by Crouch at their High Lane site, North Staffs. It is engaged on coal cleaning duties, clearing the final layer of overburden prior to O&K hydraulic face shovels being called upon to commence coal extraction.

Above: *Such was the length of time involved in the purchase, supply and erection of machines of this size that, the original purchasers, the British Steel Corporation of Scunthorpe had, in the meanwhile undergone a change of operating policy which had resulted in the closure of their iron ore mining activities. With very few operating hours recorded this Marion 7500 with 15 cu.m. bucket was obtained by Fairclough Parkinson Mining who now operate it at their Nant Helen site in South Wales. Two model 7400 Marions were also owned by this company and operated at their Blindwells, Scottish site.*

Below: *The last contract operated by Shephard Hill Mining Ltd was the Pen Bryn Oer site at Rhymney, South Wales, since re-allocated to Coal Contractors Ltd in January 1991. The Liebherr 984 series when fitted with the standard boom have a range of buckets from 2.5-6 cu.m. and feature 'Litronic' Hydraulic control. The first large Liebherr to enter the UK was a 10m. 991 purchased by Merriman Meighan Ltd. and operated near Cannock from 1982. The Aveling Barford RD series as seen here top out at 55 tonnes capacity and were an update of the 1970 Centaur range that replaced the SNs*

Above: *Having pioneered the use of articulated dump trucks in the late sixties with their DR 860A 6x4 trucks Volvo BM have, despite considerable competition, maintained their popularity for a wide range of tasks. A well used model for coal haulage is the 25 tonne capacity A25 with purpose built coal body. This example being one of the Wilson of Coylton fleet at High Lane. Wilson, a Crouch Mining subsidiary also operate a fleet of nine 325HP RR powered ERF 38 tonne trucks for hauling the coal to the Peacocks Hay disposal point.*

Below: *The Telford based Clay Colliery company, already having several Leibherr excavators in their extensive fleet purchased two thirty seven tonne Liebherr PR 751 dozers of 243KW/330HP which feature hydrostatic transmissions and currently operate on their Symon site for general duties and, when required, push loading a fleet of Terex TS24 twin powered motor scrapers. A variety of Caterpillar tractors ranging from the D5 through to the D8 constitute the rest of the dozer fleet.*

Below: *British Coal Opencast operate three Bucyrus 380Ws; one with Crouch Mining at Libry Moor, one with Miller Mining at Kirk and this one at the Coal Contractors, Rainge, Derbyshire site. With a bucket size of 9m. they are the smallest of the walking dragline range from this company. The original concept for this type of machine was for a 'one stop' operation, whereby the machine spent its entire working life in one locality, this being due to the rivetted construction method prior to the availability of arc welding. Later designs allowed for easy 'grind outs' for dismantling and re-erection at other locations but in more recent times the modular construction method has been adapted for most large machinery thus greatly reducing time spent in dismantling and rebuilding. Generator power is sometimes more suitable than mains power — which naturally entails substation construction — and for other reasons such as site layout. The N.S.M. division also operated two 10.7m. Rapier W700 modular built draglines at the nearby Godkin site but these have since been sold to the USA.*

Right: *Since introducing their first opencast size machine in the UK in 1978, the H111 of 6.5m capacity, Demag have maintained their presence with several new models in recent years. These include a 130 tonne, 10.4 m H135 for the Young Group, a 220 tonne, H185 for Wimpey Mining (as shown) making a total of five working for this company and a 320 tonne H285 for Taylor Woodrow at Butterwell. The smallest Demag mining machine currently at work here is the 85 tonne, 5.5m H85.*

Below: *General site view at the High Lane, north Staffordshire contract awarded to Crouch Mining in 1987. The high point in the history of Derek Crouch (Contractors) Ltd. occurred on their 25th anniversary in 1969 when they were producing 1.5 million tons of coal annually. The impressive statistics include a site area of 800 hectares, gross in situ excavation 200,000,000 cu.yds., coal output 6,000 tons daily and an electricity requirement equal to 11,000 houses annually. The significance of this present contract is that it commenced at the time when this once leading coal producer was acquired by Ryan International PLC., who promptly turned it around to become the top producer by 1991 with 22% of the UK output.*

Below: *Two long serving models still proving themselves capable at Brown Lees: the Terex R50 design followed on from the R45 that first appeared in 1964 and proved to be a highly successful design with an excess of 400 units having been supplied to UK opencast contractors prior to the introduction of the 33 series trucks of the seventies. The highly successful 7.5m. capacity RH75, a development of the original RH60 has achieved wide use since its introduction by Taylor Woodrow Mining Ltd. for their Butterwell contract in 1976.*

Left: *Without doubt the top selling 85 tonner of the eighties: Crouch Mining and R.J. Budge (Mining) Ltd. operate the largest UK fleets of Cat 777 and 777B trucks. For a time Caterpillar reverted to a conventional exhaust system which mounted up front created something of a noise problem but, with the return to the exhaust heated bodies this was greatly reduced. The current sound suppressed ROPS cab; an electronic monitoring system that covers the vital pressures and temperatures and an overall impressive level of performance and comfort combine to make these trucks a vast improvement over the equipment operated in the early days of opencasting.*

Below: *Short Bros. Ltd., the well known south Wales plant hire company added a new dimension to the hire industry in 1990 when they introduced the first of several Hitachi EX1800 hydraulic shovels of 10m capacity into their hire fleet. This machine went on short term hire to Crouch Mining and since then they have made an even bolder move by the introduction of a 330 tonne, 18m EX3500 shovel into the industry which traditionally caters for small to medium sized machinery requirements. This unit is currently on hire to Fairclough Parkinson Mining at their Nant Helen site in Wales along with five 130/150 tonne Cat 785 trucks, again from the Short Bros. hire fleet.*

Left and below: *With a series of 800 bore holes having proven the accessibility of 1.2 million tonnes of coal in the vicinity of the defunct Victorian Colliery near Biddulph, Staffs during the mid 80s, a contract was awarded to the Miller Mining Group Ltd. which commenced in August 1988. The Colliery spoil tip had also undergone trial boring and a further 500,000 tonnes of recoverable coal has been identified. This is being reclaimed by the use of a Derek Parnaby (International) Ltd. barrel washing plant operated by Burrows Brothers Ltd. in conjunction with Miller Mining. The coal is transported by a circuitous, but environmentally acceptable route to the Peacocks Hay Disposal Point operated by W. Todd & Co (Pemberton) Ltd. which features road and rail access. The contractors fleet of Iveco-Ford and Leyland 38 tonne trucks all exit the site via this truck wash.*

Below: *An RH120C and this 14m. capacity Demag together with two RH75s currently comprise the excavation team at Brown Lees . This model, which first arrived in the UK nearly ten years ago, has been superceded by the slightly larger H285 series of 300 tonnes approx weight. Support services have progressed along with the industry in general: the OTR company, loosely derived from the original earthmover tyre company, Booths Tyres of Nottingham, currently operate from a large number of strategically located bases with a fleet of 75 specially rigged trucks to handle all sizes of tyres for the construction and mining industry.*

Right: *Trucks that are no longer economically viable to operate gain a further lease of life by conversion into water bowsers or, to use the modern term, 'Dust Suppression Units'. This trio, from the left, are an Aveling Barford SN, Cat 769A and a Terex R50 which cater for the Brown Lees site. For small, compact sites tractor drawn tankers are usually sufficient while Cat DW21 and 631 scrapers have been adapted for larger operations. A Cat unit operated by R.J. Budge (Mining) Ltd. has been modified to provide fire fighting and power washing capabilities*

Below: *This top of the range Liebherr 984 is one of several from this marque operated by Clay Collieries Ltd. at Telford and other Midlands locations. Again, Cummins is the power unit and Litronic hydraulics handle a range of buckets from 10.5-18m. The Terex 3311E is the latest of this series of 85 tonne capacity trucks. Terex are now a member of the Northwest Engineering group which includes the Unit Rig company. As they produce a wide range of mechanical and diesel/electric drive rigid trucks and articulated coal haulers of up to 270 ton capacity it will be interesting to see if they eventually enter the 100 ton plus sector in the UK.*

Below right: *Although having only entered the opencast scene in the mid 70s R.J. Budge (Mining) Ltd. have established themselves as a major contender. They currently operate the second largest fleet of O&K excavators and, having operated a considerable number of Cat 777 trucks throughout the eighties, they purchased the first 170 ton payload 789s that arrived in 1988. This picture is dated May of that year and features one of the new arrivals at their long running West Chevington site in Northumberland*

Left: *Whilst recently working at the Crouch Mining site at High Lane, North Staffs, I encountered this tidy ex RAF Leyland Hippo fuel bowser dating from 1957. Its present duties now comprise the servicing of fuel to a fleet of fourteen Cat 777B 85 tonne dumptrucks.*

Below and bottom: *One of the team of 170 ton capacity Cat 789 trucks pictured in 1989 in use at the Budge East Pit site in West Wales. A feature of this site is the cleverly disguised fuel tanks which, apart from the obvious artistry, provided an unusual PR exercise. 45 gallon oil drums, tyres and obsolete fire extinguishers were used as a part of the 'conversions'.*

Below left: *Without doubt the top selling 85 tonner of the eighties, this 777B version at Tinsley Park is over-shadowed by the 789. However, for reasons of economy of scale (and cost) the 789s have proved more popular than the 130 ton payload 785s of which Coal Contractors Ltd. (D.P. McErlain) operated the first examples. It is probable that this will remain the most viable size for UK operations for the soon to be announced Cat 240 tonne Cat 793 and other similar types could be severely limited by the availability of sites of sufficient duration, size and location.*

Below: *By contrast — state of the art earthmoving in the 90s. The thirteen strong fleet of Cat 170 tonne capacity model 789 trucks, two O&K RH200 shovels and a 120 backhoe which comprise the main fleet at Stobswood. As and when required a further two trucks will be introduced. Although Crouch Mining have considerable expertise in maintaining and repairing a wide variety of heavy plant the current trend appears to be in favour of lease hiring followed up with contract maintenance provided by the manufacturers or their distributors.*

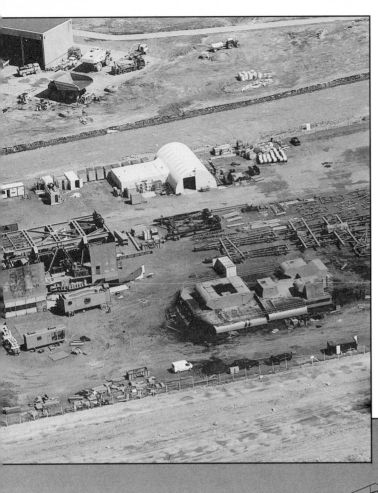

The ultimate earthmoving machine in the UK must be the Page 757 walking dragline commissioned by British Coal Opencast and Crouch mining at Stobswood on December 5th 1991. At a cost of £16m and weighing in excess of 4000 tonnes , it takes over the UK heavy weight title from the recently retired 'Big Geordie' at the nearby Taylor Woodrow 'Butterwell' site. No doubt partially influenced by the availability of the 50 cu. m/65 cu yd buckets as used by the 'Big Geordie', an operational policy was adopted to remain at this working capacity rather than utilise the 75 cu. yd. rating of the 'Ace of Spades'. With a working life of at least 10 years at Stobswood greatly reduced periods of down time are envisaged by this conservative operating capacity. Thanks to the goodwill of Ivan Jameson and Martin Thomas of B.C.O. and George Murray, plant manager at the time, I was able to view this behemoth at close range earlier in the year and, although having been aboard several large machines previously this was something else! One item of interest that is not usually associated with this type of machinery in years past was the inclusion of an industrial vacuum cleaner which the attendants would no doubt find very useful in maintaining a clean interior which is of detached house proportions!

Above: *The first 400+ tonne RH200 was delivered to Budge in 1989 for operation at West Chevington, with its 20m bucket it became an ideal match for the 789 trucks and, depending on conditions, a three pass load is obtained. Their second unit operates at the Tinsley Park 1.5m. ton contract to reclaim the old steel works and provide a novel form of after use by way of a short take-off and load (STOL) airport for Sheffield Corporation. Budge are currently number two B.C.O. contractor with 15% of the total coal output for 1991.*

Below: *An obvious publicity shot from O&K. With the modular method of construction very much in vogue nowadays, illustrations such as this highlight the ease of erection which, added to the much shorter erection time are greatly reducing the requirement for excessively costly indivisible or abnormal load movements.*

Restoration & Reclamation

One of the most vital and certainly most noticeable aspects of the opencast coal extraction process is the final re-instatement of worked out or derelict areas: consequently, in keeping with increasing public awareness and advancing technology, considerable time, effort and expense have been devoted to this phase of the operation.

Coal extraction and the subsequent restoration processes are subject to consultation with, and the approval of, up to 25 Governmental bodies and private agencies with the Ministry of Agriculture, Fisheries and Food and the Mineral Planning Authority being two of the most prominent. The Agricultural Development Advisory Service (A.D.A.S.) as an agency of the M.A.F.F., monitor all operations where agriculture and related land is involved and also administer a 5 year rehabilitation and after-care period in order to return the soil to a satisfactory level of productivity as soon as possible.

With the recent lessening in demand for home produced foodstuffs, alternatives have been initiated in suitable areas and include areas for wildlife, forestry, social amenity and the industrial applications including roads, housing and numerous commercial applications including an airport.

For agricultural purposes, topsoil and subsoil are removed and stored separately at the start and, on completion are replaced with low ground pressure machinery to alleviate soil structure damage and excessive compaction. A typical example being the Bateswood site near Newcastle-u-Lyme, now returned to a mixture of agricultural, forestry, wildlife and leisure applications with participation from the Staffordshire Wildlife Trust.

Industrial examples in the country include the removal of a vast area of dereliction left over from the former Birchenwood Coking plant and which now features housing and sports fields, altogether a vast improvement. Another example being a much needed replacement length of the B5367 road which was incorporated into the standard backfill operation at the High Lane site, thereby eliminating public expenditure. Both of these operations involved the usual stringent compaction procedures as specified for industrial applications.

Above and over page: *Simba Machinery Ltd., in conjunction with British Coal Opencast and other involved bodies, design and build machinery specifically for restoration applications including, heavy duty discs, subsoilers and tillage equipment. Ingersoll Rand are also major suppliers with their compaction equipment whilst plant from other manufacturers includes tree transplanters and wide-track drainage machines.*